Music for Me

Picture Songbook

Lorna Lutz Heyge

Linda Swears

Illustrated by

Deborah and Allan Drew-Brooke-Cormack

Beginnings

MUSIC RESOURCES INTERNATIONAL
Walton, New York, U.S.A.   Toronto, Ontario, Canada

Music for Me

ISBN 0-945613-13-X

Credits:
Calico Pony is copyrighted by Wide World Music, Inc., of Delaware Water Gap, Pa., and used by permission.

Tap your sticks till the music stops.

Shoe a little horse,
Shoe a little mare,
But let the little colt
Go bare,
     bare,
          bare!

This is baby ready for a nap.
  Lay her down in her mother's lap.
Cover her up so she won't peep.
  Rock her till she's fast asleep.

Bye lo, Baby-o;
  Off to dreamland you must go.

I'm riding my pony,
My calico pony.
We travel together
Wherever we go.

I love that old pony,
That calico pony.
If you want to buy him,
The answer is "no."

See how I'm jumping,
 Jumping, jumping.
See how I'm bouncing
 Like a ball.
You didn't know
 I could jump so high.
You didn't know
 I could stand so still.

See how I'm jumping,
 Jumping, jumping.
When I am tired
 Down I flop.

Ring around the rosey.
  A pocket full of posies.
Ashes, ashes,
  We all fall down.

Tapping at the window,
  Tapping at the door.
Everybody jumps up
  When we count to four.
      1,   2,   3,   4!

Bow wow wow.
Who's dog art thou?
I am Tommy's dog,
Bow wow wow.

Baby's
Almost
Sleeping

Hop, Old Squirrel

Two little apples hanging on a tree.
Two little apples smiling at me.

I shook that tree as hard as I could.
Down came the apples, Mm! Mm! Good!

Do you know the muffin man,
The muffin man,
The muffin man?
Do you know the muffin man
Who lives in Drury Lane?

Oh, my!
  No more pie.
Pie's too sweet,
  I wanna piece of meat.
Meat's too red,
  I wanna piece of bread.
Bread's too brown,
  I think I'll go to town.
Town's too far,
  I think I'll take a car.
Car won't go,
  I fell and stubbed my toe.
Toe gives me pain,
  I think I'll take a train.
Train had a wreck,
  I fell and broke my neck.
Oh, my!
  No more pie.

May there always be sunshine,
May there always be blue skies,
May there always be mama,
May there always be me.

Somebody's knocking at my door.
Somebody's knocking at my door.
O children, I hear you knocking.
Somebody's knocking at my door.

Rub - a - dub - dub.

It's fun to take a bath.

Look what I can do!

These are Grandma's
    glasses.
This is Grandma's
    hat.
This is the way
    she folds
    her hands
And lays them in her
    lap.

These are Grandpa's
    glasses.
This is Grandpa's
    hat.
This is the way
    he folds
    his arms
Just like that.

Peanut, peanut butter, and jelly!

First you dig 'em.
  Then you crack 'em.
Then you squish 'em.
  Then you stir 'em.

Then you spread it.
Then you chew it.
Then you eat it.

Let's shake
our
bells
together

Because
it's
fun
to do.

Bell horses, bell horses,
What's the time of day?
One o'clock, two o'clock,
Time to go away!